ASIAPAC COMIC

THE BOOK OF
ZEN
Freedom of the Mind

禅说

Edited & Illustrated by **TSAI CHIH CHUNG**

Translated by Koh Kok Kiang

ASIAPAC • SINGAPORE

Publisher

ASIAPAC BOOKS PTE LTD

996 Bendemeer Road #06-08/09 Singapore 339944

Tel: (65) 6392 8455 Fax: (65) 6392 6455

Email: asiapacbooks@pacific.net.sg

Visit us at our Internet home page
www.asiapacbooks.com

First published July 1990
12th edition May 2004

© 1990 ASIAPAC BOOKS, SINGAPORE
ISBN 9971-985-48-9

Bibliographic Data

```
LDR         nam a    00
001         ASP1003
005         20011009101348.0
008         010929s1990    si a          000 0 eng d
020         ‡a9971985489 (pbk.)
041   1     ‡aeng‡hchi
050   14    ‡aBQ9265.8‡b.C35 1990
082   0     ‡a294.3927‡221
100   1     ‡aCai, Zhizhong,‡d1948-
245   14    ‡aThe book of Zen :‡bfreedom of the mind /‡cedited &
            illustrated by Tsai Chih Chung ; translated by Koh Kok
            Kiang.
260         ‡aSingapore :‡bAsiapac,‡c1990.
300         ‡a151 p. :‡bchiefly ill. ;‡c21 cm.
490   1     ‡aAsiapac comic series
650   0     ‡aZen Buddhism‡vHumor.
700   1     ‡aKoh, Kok Kiang.
800   1     ‡aCai, Zhizhong,‡d1948-‡tAsiapac comic series.
```

Edited by C T Choo
Cover design by Illusion Creative Studio
Typeset by Superskill Graphics
Printed in Singapore by Chung Printing

AcuMedic CENTRE
101-105 CAMDEN HIGH STREET
LONDON NW1 7JN
Tel: 020 7388-6704/5783
info@acumedic.com www.acumedic.com

Publisher's Note

Comics play an important role in our fast-moving urban society. They serve the young as well as the adult readers. Comics are not only fun and entertaining, they can also be a kind of political satire and can even make classical literature and philosophy available to us in a light-hearted way.

As a publisher who is always on the look-out for the readers' needs, we are pleased to present you **Asiapac Comic Series**. We hope this series will bring you many hours of entertainment and enlightenment.

We feel honoured to have well-known Taiwanese cartoonist Tsai Chih Chung's permission to the translation right to his best-selling comics. We would also like to take this opportunity to thank the translators and typesetters for putting in their best efforts in the production of this series.

Asiapac's new corporate identity design

The Asiapac Books corporate symbol has its original inspiration from the Chinese character for Asia. The central globe symbolizes the international market for which we publish and distribute books, thereby helping to bridge the East and the West. The open book resembling soaring wings represents Asiapac, ever dynamic and innovative, aiming to communicate with modern society through the printed page. The green colour expresses Asiapac's commitment to go "green for life".

About the Author / Illustrator

Tsai Chih Chung was born in 1948 in Chang Hwa County of Taiwan. He began drawing cartoon strips at the age of 17 and worked as Art Director for Kuang Chi Programme Service in 1971. He founded the Far East Animation Production Company and the Dragon Cartoon Production Company in 1976, where he produced two cartoon films entitled *Old Master Q* and *Shao Lin Temple*.

Tsai Chih Chung first got his four-box comics published in newspapers and magazines in 1983. His funny comic characters such as the Drunken Swordsman, Fat Dragon, One-eyed Marshal and Bold Supersleuth have been serialized in newspapers in Singapore, Malaysia, Taiwan, Hong Kong, Japan, Europe and the United States.

He was voted one of the Ten Outstanding Young People of Taiwan in 1985 and was acclaimed by the media and the academic circle in Taiwan.

The comic book *The Sayings of Zhuang Zi* was published in 1986 and marked a milestone in Tsai's career. Within two years, *Zhuang Zi* went into more than 70 reprints in Taiwan and 15 in Hong Kong and has to date sold over one million copies.

In 1987, Tsai Chih Chung published *The Sayings of Lao Zi*, *The Sayings of Confucius* and two books based on Zen. Since then, he has published more than 20 titles, out of which 10 are about ancient Chinese thinkers and the rest based on historical and literary classics. All these books topped the bestsellers' list at one time or another. They have been translated into other languages such as Japanese, Korean and Thai. Asiapac is the publisher for the English version of these comics.

Tsai Chih Chung can be said to be the pioneer in the art of visualizing Chinese literature and philosophy by way of comics.

Foreword

What is Zen? One might as well ask: What is life?

And life is to be lived, if possible, at the fullest level — not made into a matter of theories of living and what not.

Zen shuns abstract explanations, idle philosophical speculations and all kinds of pretensions, for they are far removed from the throb of life.

The bulk of Zen literature, in all of its astonishing variety of forms, deals with nothing but misconceptions about the essence of Zen. The apparent complexity of Zen teaching and function is due to the complexity of human mentality, and Zen is an illustration of "skill in means" in dealing with complex minds.

Its only concern is to help one, through awareness and enlightenment, to realize one's human potential completely — to flower in goodness as a human being.

Zen masters stressed that the buddhas began as human beings, that enlightenment is within reach in a single lifetime for those dedicated and diligent enough. "A complete human being is a buddha, a complete buddha is a human being."

Zen lends itself very well to illustration in cartoon form, for Zen has a natural simplicity and a direct and down-to-earth approach to living that is at once refreshing and illuminating.

Zen means to be free — absolutely — to be a human being, and this is possible only when self-interest has ended and a person is one with the immensity of life.

The mind of modern people may be very advanced technologically, but it remains heavily thought-laden and thus lacking in clarity. So it is probably just as well that a book on Zen should appear in the form of cartoons.

Hopefully, reading a book of cartoons will give the reader a delightful break from his deep involvement in the thought process — something which the Zen masters aver is a liability rather than an asset. (To give an illustration of the limitation of living by thought, we feel miserable and have no heart for anything else while grappling with some kind of personal problem which we feel helpless about — frustration arising from an unfulfilled desire, a relationship gone awry, etc.). The Zen way of living would be "no ego, no problem."

Translating Tsai Chih Chung's book was for this reason an enjoyable experience. The Zen anecdotes and parables depicted in the book span a period of more than 2,000 years, from the time when Shakyamuni Buddha transmitted "the teaching that is beyond words" to the time of the Japanese Zen masters of the 19th century.

Tsai Chih Chung based his cartoons on a wide variety of Zen texts and compilations. The main ones from which he picked examples are: *Zen Flesh, Zen Bones* (in English) by Nyogen Senzaki and Paul Reps; the *Jingde Chuandenglu* (Record Concerning the Passing On of the Lamp, composed in the Jingde Period), the earliest historical work of Zen literature compiled in the year 1004; and two of the most important Zen koan collections, the *Biyenlu* (Blue Cliff Record), and the *Wumenguan* (Gateless Gate).

Koh Kok Kiang

About the Translator

Koh Kok Kiang is a journalist by vocation and a quietist by inclination. He is a sub-editor with *The Straits Times* of Singapore. His interest in cultural topics and things of the mind started in his schooling years. It was his wish to discover the wisdom of the East that kindled his interest in Eastern philosophy.

Contents

Zen 禅

What is Zen? 何谓禅?   13

Realization of the wave 波浪的觉悟   14

Zen in a teacup 杯茶禅理   15

Result of enlightenment 悟道的结果   16

The sayings of Zen 禅说   17

Heart to heart 以心传心   18

To live in the "now" 把握现时   20

Kasyapa 迦叶杀竿   21

Carrying a girl across the stream 渡女过河   22

Heaven and hell 天堂之门   23

Blockhead Official 呆头大官   24

If I do not enter hell, who will? 我不入地狱谁入地狱   25

Colours of the bamboos 墨竹朱竹   26

Order in life and death 生死有序   27

Breaking the silence 不悟戒   28

All is emptiness 一切皆空   29

Buddha at home 佛在家中   30

Finger pointing at the moon 指月的喻语   31

The fallible disciple 迷途的学子   32

Thief who learnt his lesson 强盗的觉悟   33

Wide off the mark 说是一物即不中   34

The mute and the parrot 哑吧和鹦鹉   35

Death of a teacup 茶杯禅理   36

Who is he? 不识头衔   37

Coming to terms with oneself 物我对立   38

Fatal words 言过其行   40

The sound of the valley 山谷之音   41

Fate is in one's own hands 命运在自己手里   42

The greater the haste, the slower it is 愈急愈慢   44

The general's antique 将军的古玩   45

Giving and receiving 施与受   46

A friend after one's own heart 知音人   47

The light has been extinguished 盲人不知灯熄   48

Things of real worth 值钱的东西   49

A blade of grass, a drop of water 一枝草一点露   50

Not because of anything 不为任何   51

Past, present, and future 过去现在未来   52

Great waves of the mind 心中的大浪   53

Because I am here 因为我在   56

Emptiness 色即是空   57

Buddha or demon, all in a thought 成佛成魔一念间   58

The unruffled heart 至人用心若镜   59

Mountain dharma is constant 山径不变   60

The lovesick monk 违顺相争   61

Where does one go after death? 死后何处去   62

The swordless sword 无剑之剑   63

Fanning the flames 轻轻一拨扇   64

The demon within 魔由心生   65

Poverty and wealth 贫与富   66

Hand of generosity 不执着两边   67

Never static but constantly changing 不变应万变   68

Laughter that unites heaven and earth 天地同笑   70

Zen cannot be spoken of 禅不可说   71

Cloud in the clear sky, water in the pitcher 云在青天水在瓶   72

Snowflakes 好雪片片   73

Zhaozhou's stone bridge 赵州石桥   74

Go wash the bowl 洗钵去   75

Where to practise Zen? 如何修行   76

The cypress tree and Buddhahood 柏树子成佛   77

The many return to the One 多归於一   78

What is Zhaozhou? 如何是赵州   79

Zhaozhou finding out about Zhaozhou 赵州问赵州   80

The cypress tree in the courtyard 庭前柏树子　　81

No substitute 代替不来　　82

Not attached to anything 不持一物　　83

Have a cup of tea 喝茶去　　84

Deshan Xuanjian 德山宣鉴　　85

Linji Yixuan 临济义玄　　89

Whiplash 投鞭断流　　91

Not to be dependent is to be saved 无依无求　　92

What is living and what is dying? 何谓生何谓死　　93

Juzhi's one-finger Zen 俱胝一指弹　　95

Juzhi cuts off disciple's finger 俱胝断指　　99

Xiangyan's man up a tree 香严上树　　100

Same destination, different paths 目标相同路不同　　101

Six in One 六根合一　　102

Too near and cannot see 视而不见　　103

The universe in a mustard seed 芥纳须弥　　104

The monk who lacks compassion 枯木禅　　105

True self, awake! 主人公　　106

Simple truth but difficult to follow 白发居士　　107

Ordinary-mindedness is the way 平常心　　108

Which one is not the best? 那个不是精底　　109

The fragrance of the osmanthus 木犀香自香　　110

Tall and short bamboo 高竹低竹　　111

No me, no other 无我无他　　112

I am here 我在　　113

Jingqing and the sound of raindrops 镜清雨滴声　　114

Not seeing the truth 不识"真我"　　115

To lack nothing 空手而回　　116

Beyond words 阴雨两人行　　117

There is and there is not 有与无　　118

Follow the flow 随流去　　119

Difficult to advance and to retreat 进退两难　　120

Monk without a sense of humour 不如小丑　　121

9

Danxia burning a Buddha statue 丹霞烧佛 123

Act according to circumstances 心随境移 124

Oneness with the universe 心境如一 125

Change is the eternal truth 山花开似锦 126

What is not the dharma? 什么不是佛法 127

To grasp nothingness 抓住虚空 128

The fire spirit comes for fire 火神求火 129

The way to truth is right before you 眼前问即是道路 131

Dongshan's "no cold or heat" 寒时寒杀阇黎 132

The nun becomes a monk 尼姑变和尚 133

Three pounds of hemp 麻三斤 134

Buffalo passing through a window 牛过窗櫺 136

To be master of oneself 做自己的主人公 137

A day of wind and rain 一朝风月 138

The snake's two conflicting heads 蛇的两头 140

The frogs' soliloquy 青蛙的独白 142

The spider's lifeline 蜘蛛之丝 144

Luosheng gate 罗生门 148

The Book of
Zen

Zen in a teacup

Result of enlightenment

1 Since olden times, many people have left their homes and families to enter the door of Buddhism and practise Zen.

Tong! Tong! Tong!

2 They do not mind devoting so much energy to inquiry and contemplation, and what do they gain from it?

3 If such a question is put to the Zen masters, they will invariably answer:

4
* Nothingness
無 Wu

Once a person has stopped discrimination, banished delusion, and ended the tricks of thought, he will be full of inner peace and there is naturally the state of nothingness.

* The Chinese character 'wu' can also mean "enlightenment."

16

THE SAYINGS OF ZEN

Heart to heart

1
When Shakyamuni Buddha was in Gridhrakuta (Spirit Peak) Mountain, he seated himself on a platform, as if about to give a talk.

2
Suddenly Shakyamuni took out a flower and watched his disciples for their reaction. The onlookers did not understand the Buddha's action and stared at him in silence.

3
Only Kasyapa smiled at this revelation.

4

5. My way of understanding is to perceive thoroughly the process of thought and exclude nothing, and with a joyous heart look into the actual nature of things.

6. Such a subtle dharma is beyond words, beyond philosophical speculation.

7. One cannot understand it through logical reasoning, but only through insight.

8. Just now, Kasyapa responded and showed his understanding, therefore I will transmit to him the heart of Zen.

The way of Zen is: The uncontaminated divine law and the uncontaminated heart bring forth perception and insight, and right living is naturally sustained.

*Note: The flag-pole was one set up at a temple gate to show, by the raising of a flag, that teaching was going on - a silent signal that instruction was being offered by an accredited teacher.

26

Breaking the silence

1 Four monks made an agreement to meditate in silence for a week and not to speak a single word.

2 On the first day, they maintained silence. But as darkness fell, the flame of the candle began to flicker ...

3 Oh, the flame is going out.

4 Eh, we should not speak a single word.

5 Why do you two want to talk?

6 Ha! Ha! Ha! I am the only one who did not talk.

Many people, in admonishing others and pointing out their errors, very likely are themselves fallible.

All is emptiness

1
A young Japanese student of Zen, Yamaoka Tesshu, visited one master after another. One day, he called upon Dokuon of Shokoku.

2
He wanted to show his attainment and was full of pride.

The mind, Buddha, sentient beings, after all, do not exist.

3
The true nature of phenomena is emptiness. There is no realization, no delusion, no wisdom, no mediocrity. There is no giving and nothing to be received.

4
Tok!
Ouch!

5
Why did you hit me?

If nothing exists, where did this great anger come from?

6
"No good, no evil, no sorrow, no happiness, all is emptiness." This profound statement is not even understood by ordinary people. The Zen uttered by Yamaoka Tesshu is but empty words.

Buddha at home

Yang Pu left home and went to Sichuan Province with the intention of visiting a bodhisattva.

1

Where are you going?

I want to be a disciple of a bodhisattva.

2

Instead of searching for a bodhisattva, isn't it far better to seek Buddha?

Where is Buddha to be found?

3

When you reach home and find yourself being greeted by a person wrapped with a blanket and wearing shoes in the wrong order, that person is Buddha.

Yes.

4

5

He followed the instructions and when he returned home it was already nightfall.

6 His mother, on hearing her son's voice at the door, was so happy that she was in too much of a rush to get dressed, so she threw a blanket around herself and even wore her shoes in the wrong order. She rushed out to open the door and when Yang Pu saw his mother, he was dumbfounded.

One may travel far and wide in search of truth but he must realize it in himself or he will find it not.

The fallible disciple

When Japanese Zen master Bankei Eitaku held retreats, pupils from all over Japan came to attend.

Caught you in the act of stealing money again!

Disgusting!

Do forgive him, please!

No way! He has been let off many times already. This time he cannot be forgiven again.

If you do not expel him, we shall all leave together.

You are wise brothers; you can tell right from wrong, but he does not even know right and wrong. If I do not instruct him, who will?

I am going to keep him here. Even if all of you leave the temple, it makes no difference.

In a flock of one hundred sheep, one goes missing. A thorough search is made for that lost sheep while the other ninety-nine are left untended in the pasture or wilderness. Help the one that needs help most.

Upon hearing these words, the thieving monk threw himself to the ground with tears streaming down his face. He resolved never to commit a wrongdoing again.

Thief who learnt his lesson

Panel 1

A thief confronted Japanese Zen master Shichiri Kojun.

Hand over your money, or I will take your old life!

Panel 2

The money is in the drawer. Get it yourself but leave a little behind for me to buy food.

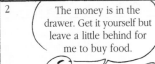

Panel 3

After receiving things from others, you ought to say thank you.

Thank you!

Panel 4

Eventually the thief was arrested ...

He stole your money, right?

Panel 5

He did not steal from me. I gave him the money and he also thanked me.

Panel 6

After he had completed his prison term, the man immediately went to Shichiri and begged to be accepted as his disciple.

"Putting aside the butcher's knife and instantly becoming a buddha" is extremely difficult to realize in practice. What power is it that compels one to lay down the butcher's knife? Compassion - that is all!

The mute and the parrot

When a man realizes that *there is*, but does not know how to express it, what is he like?

Xuekuai asked Huilin Cishou:

He is like a mute who has tasted honey.

When a man who actually does not realize that *there is*, yet talks glibly about it, what would he be like?

How are you? How are you?

He is like a parrot greeting people.

One has to appear to be like a mute in learning Zen; to be inwardly whole, yet by conventional standards one seems to suffer deficiency. The worst is one who is impoverished inwardly and, like a parrot, talks meaninglessly. This is merely mouthing Zen.

Coming to terms with oneself

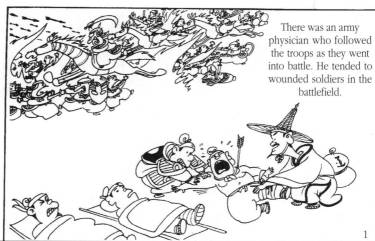

There was an army physician who followed the troops as they went into battle. He tended to wounded soldiers in the battlefield.

1

2

Whenever his patients had recovered from their injuries, they were once again sent to continue fighting. As a result, they were wounded once again or killed ...

3

After seeing this scenario again and again, he eventually suffered a mental breakdown.

4

If he is fated to die, why should I save him? If my medical knowledge has any meaning, why must he go into battle and lose his life?

Fatal words

1. There was a wealthy old lady who often went to the temple to pray. Whenever she knelt in front of the statue of Buddha, she would say: "I am now so advanced in years, you can claim my life any time you wish. Amitabha Buddha!"

2. I will play a prank on her.

3. "I am now so advanced in years; you can claim my life any time you wish. Amitabha Buddha!" Hee! Hee!

4. Old lady, in that case please come over tonight!

Wow!

5. The old lady died of shock.

Nice-sounding words intended to sway others are of questionable value and often lead to mishap. Not saying what is false is the foundation for right action.

The sound of the valley

1. Once there was a Buddhist devotee who went into the mountains to visit a Zen master and ask him about the gateway to Zen.

2. On your way here, you passed through the valley, right?

   Yes.

3. Did you hear the sound of the valley?

4. Yes, I heard it.

5. In that case, the source from which you heard the sound of the valley is the gateway to Zen.

   There is wonder in the budding of flowers, there is beauty in the falling of flowers. To be able to perceive the beauty of the things all around is to enter the gateway of Zen.

Fate is in one's own hands

1 In ancient times, there was a general who led his troops to fight the enemy whose strength was greater than his by tenfold.

On the way, he stopped at a shrine to pray and seek guidance.

2

3 Now I am going to toss a coin. If head comes, we will win. If tail comes, we will lose.

4 Our lives are in the hands of destiny.

45

Giving and receiving

1. I am getting old. I am going to give you a book of teachings to represent your successorship.

The Japanese Zen master Bunan Shido had only one dharma successor, Shoju Rojin.

2. I received your Zen without written words and I am satisfied with it as it is. You had better keep the book.

3. This book has been handed down for seven generations, so you ought to keep it as a symbol of having received the teachings. Here.

Very well.

4. !

5. What are you doing?

6. What are you saying?

Understanding and action are one. If one expounds the teachings but does not live them, then it is just like merely mouthing Zen.

A friend after one's own heart

1 Bo Ya was a skilful zither player and his friend Zhong Ziqi had a fine ear for the music of the zither.

2 Whenever Bo Ya played a tune about the mountains ...

Lovely indeed! It is as lofty as Mount Taishan.

3 And whenever Bo Ya played a tune about the flowing waters ...

Wonderful indeed! It's as meandering as the Changjiang and the Yellow River.

4 Eventually Zhong Ziqi fell ill and died. Bo Ya never played his zither again.

5 He slashed the strings of his zither. Since that time, "cutting the zither's strings" has always been used to describe friendship.

A friend after one's own heart is hard to find. After the death of his good friend, although Bo Ya was still hale and hearty, it was as if half of him had departed.

47

The light has been extinguished

1 As a blind man was taking leave of his friend, the friend gave him a lantern.

I do not need the lantern. Light or darkness makes no difference to me.

2 Yes, I know that. But if you do not take it with you, others may bump into you in the dark.

Alright!

3

4 Aiyah! Aiyah!

5 Can't you see the lantern?

6 The light in your lantern went out long ago.

Those who make use of the words of others to instruct people can be likened to the blind man. The light of his lantern had gone out long ago, yet he was himself unaware of it.

48

Things of real worth

1 A thief went to the home of Japanese Zen master Ryokan Daigu, who lived the simplest kind of life in a little hut at the foot of a mountain.

However, the thief found nothing of value in the hut.

2

3 You have come a long way here and should not return empty-handed. Here, take this robe with you.

4

5 Poor fellow, it is a pity I cannot present him with this beautiful moon.

Most people only pursue wealth and status, but in the world how much can one acquire? The stars, the moon, mountains and flowing waters, each flower and blade of grass are all there for you to appreciate.

A blade of grass, a drop of water

1 Yes! This is just right.

Japanese Zen master Gisan was taking a bath. Because the water was too hot, he asked his disciple to add some cold water ...

2 !

3 You dunce! Everything can be put to good use. Even trees like to have water, there is life in water.

4 Why did you not give the rest of the water to the plants? What right have you to waste even a drop of water?

5 The disciple became awakened in that instant. He changed his name to Tekisui, meaning "a drop of water."

All things have their uses. However humble its origin, every little thing has a place in nature.

Not because of anything

51

Past, present and future

1
Buddha told a parable:
A man encountered a tiger in the wilderness ...

Help!

2
He ran to a cliff and with both hands grabbed hold of an over-hanging vine while the tiger growled menacingly below with its jaws wide open.

3
Two mice, one white and one black, began to gnaw away at the vine.

4
Rip!

Oh!

5
Suddenly, he saw a luscious strawberry near him.

6
He plucked the strawberry and popped it into his mouth ...

Such an exquisite taste!

Not to think about the past and the future, but to cherish one moment after another is real fortune.

Great waves of the mind

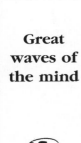

1 There was a wrestler named "Great Waves." He was immensely strong and knew the art of wrestling.

2 In his private bouts, he was so powerful that even his teacher was no match for him.

3 But in public he was so bashful that even his own pupils defeated him.

Lost!

4 He therefore went into the mountains to seek the advice of a Zen master.

5 Your name is Great Waves. Imagine that you are those billows. You are those huge waves sweeping everything before them, swallowing all in their path. You are no longer a wrestler who is afraid.

6 Do this and you will be the greatest wrestler in the land. No one will be able to defeat you.

Yes!

8 Great Waves remained in the temple sitting in meditation, trying to imagine himself as waves. At first his mind was restless and he thought about all kinds of things. Before long ...

9

10 He turned more and more to the feeling of the waves.

11 As night advanced the waves became larger and larger. They swept away the flower vases and the Buddhist statues ...

Emptiness

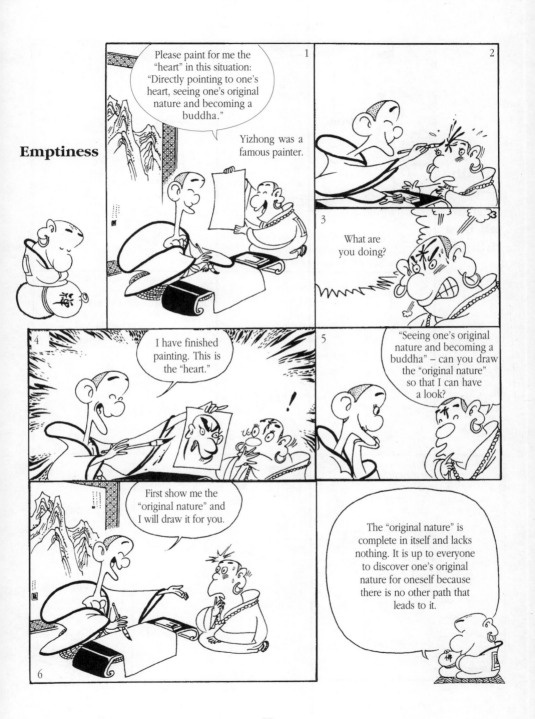

Buddha or demon, all in a thought

1

There was an old woman nicknamed "Weeping Hag." She cried when it rained, she also cried when it did not rain.

I have two daughters, the elder sells cloth shoes and the younger sells umbrellas.

Old lady, what are you crying for?

2

3

When the weather is fine, I think of my younger daughter whose umbrellas are not in demand.

When it rains, I think of my elder daughter. During rainy days, no customers will want to go to her shop to buy shoes.

4

You should think of business being good for your elder daughter when the weather is fine. During rainy days, your younger daughter's umbrellas will definitely sell well.

Oh! You are right!

5

6

Since then, "Weeping Hag" no longer cried. She smiled at all times - rain or shine.

"Approaching the heart is approaching buddhahood." Whether something is favourable or unfavourable depends on how you look at it.

Mountain dharma is constant

1
There was a general who often fought fiercely to kill enemies in the battlefield.

2
As he grew older, he felt that the events in life were ephemeral and thus embraced Buddhism.

3
He was often asked by people why he changed his life and he replied:

4
The mountain and the way of the mountain do not change. What has changed is my heart.

5
The straightforward man painstakingly observes himself and is true to himself. So when he is a layman, he acts like a layman. When he is a monk, he acts like one.

The lovesick monk

1. The Japanese nun Eshun was very beautiful. During a dharma lecture, a monk secretly fell in love with her.

2. Ah!

3. He wrote her a love letter, requesting a private meeting.

4. The following day, the Zen master gave a lecture and when it was over, Eshun arose. Addressing the monk who had written her the love letter, she said:

5. If you really love me so much, come and embrace me now.

Human nature is characterized by conflict, the state of being torn between opposing desires. This leads to disharmony of the mind. Therefore one has to be unceasingly aware at all times.

Where does one go after death?

The Japanese Emperor Goyozei was studying Zen under Zen master Gudo Toshoku.

In Zen this very mind is Buddha. Is this correct?

1

If I say yes, you will think that you understand without understanding. If I say no, I would be contradicting a fact which many understand quite well.

2

Where does the enlightened man go when he dies?

3

I know not.

When living, one should appreciate life's beauty and mystery from the standpoint of being alive. There is no need to be concerned about the world after death. When it is today, live for today. There is no need to be depressed over tomorrow because tomorrow's events will come tomorrow.

Why don't you know?

Because I have not died yet.

5

6

Fanning the flames

When Zen master Dahui Zonggao of the Song Dynasty was meditating in the mountain wilderness, a former general expressed a wish to leave home and become a monk.

When I have got rid of my bad habits, I will come to follow you, master.

Good.

1

Master, I have got rid of my ego, and come specially to embrace Zen.

It is still too early for that destiny. Your wife is sleeping with another man.

2

3

Which bald head dares to utter nonsense?

It is still far too early for you to leave home. Go back and practise for a few more years before you think about leaving home.

Words and actions are two manifestations of one's state of mind. But with most people, there are more words than actions, or even actions that contradict words.

4

5

64

The demon within

1. There was a monk who always encountered a gigantic spider that bothered him just as he began to meditate.

2. I see ...

   Once I begin to meditate, the giant spider appears and no matter what I do to chase it away, it just would not go.

3. Next time when you begin to meditate, have a brush ready. If the spider comes again, you draw a big circle on its body to leave a mark so that you can later trace where that strange creature came from.

   Yes!

4. The monk did as he was told. When he drew a big circle on the spider's body, the spider went away and he could continue meditating.

5. When he had finished his meditation, the monk was bewildered to see the big circle on his own belly.

   Ho! Ho!

   In human life, one encounters many vexations and perturbations. The worst vexations are usually brought about by oneself.

Poverty and wealth

1

Wah! A gold lohan.

There was a farmer who dug up a very valuable gold lohan statue in the mountain wilderness.

2

Hee! Hee! Now we can enjoy all we want for the rest of our lives.

It must weigh at least fifty kg of solid gold.

His family, relatives and friends felt very happy for him.

3

But this farmer was not happy. He pulled a long face the whole day and kept on sighing ...

4

You are now a millionaire. What is there left for you to be depressed about?

How depressing!

5

Because I do not know where the other seventeen lohans* are to be found.

True wealth is not in how much riches one has, but whether one knows contentment.

*In Chinese Buddhist lore, there are said to be 18 lohans in all.

Laughter that unites heaven and earth

1

One evening, Zen master Yaoshan Weiyan of the Tang Dynasty walked up to the mountain.

2

Suddenly, the clouds and mist lifted, revealing the bright moon. Yaoshan burst into laughter.

3

Ha! Ha!

4

His laughter was so loud that it could be heard at the village below.

5

Last night, I suddenly heard loud laughter. I wonder where it came from?

I heard it too.

6

That was the sound of our master laughing on the mountain last night.

In whatever situations, as long as there is no "me," you are not separate from the thing. Yaoshan's laughter, in which the self was absent, became one with heaven and earth.

Zen cannot
be spoken of

Snowflakes

1 Layman Pangyun, an enlightened lay person, visited the monk Yaoshan and when he was about to leave, Yaoshan asked the Zen wayfarers to send him off.

Please send off the guest on my behalf.

Yes.

2

3 Beautiful snowflakes one and all, each one falling where it should fall ...

4 Where do they fall?

5

6 Your eyes see like a blind man's; your mouth speaks like a mute's. How dare you call yourself a Zen wayfarer?

All things in the world, whether big or small, valuable or not, have their uses. Each has its place. Why ask why they are just right? It has always been so!

Zhaozhou's stone bridge

1 Rumour has it that the Guanyin Temple in Hebei Province has the very famous Zhaozhou stone bridge ...

2 You see only the wooden bridge. You cannot see Zhaozhou's stone bridge.

I heard that this place has a Zhaozhou stone bridge, but all I saw was just a log bridge. Where is the stone bridge?

3 What actually is Zhaozhou's stone bridge?

4 The one that acts as a bridge for donkeys, horses and all other "lost" people.

The wooden bridge which has a form has only limited use in helping people cross over to a point. The formless stone bridge of Zhaozhou is the bodhisattva's compassionate nature that benefits all beings.

Go wash
the bowl

1

A man became a monk at the Guanyin Temple. He met the abbot, Zhaozhou Congshen of the Tang Dynasty.

2

It is the first time your disciple is here. Please give me some guidance, master.

3

Yes, I have eaten.

Have you eaten the porridge?

4

Then go wash the bowl.

Perception, practice of Zen and everyday action are the same thing. It is vital to understand this point. To be absolutely alert is practising Zen; it is not that in making an effort to practise one then gains insight.

Where to practise Zen?

The cypress tree and Buddhahood

77

The many return to the One

All things return to the One. To what does the One return?

When I was in Qingzhou district, I made a hemp robe that weighed seven pounds.

The source of all things produces myriad forms, each distinctive, and yet all these things have the same origin. The One and the many are not separate but in harmony. If the many return to the One, then the One also returns to the many.

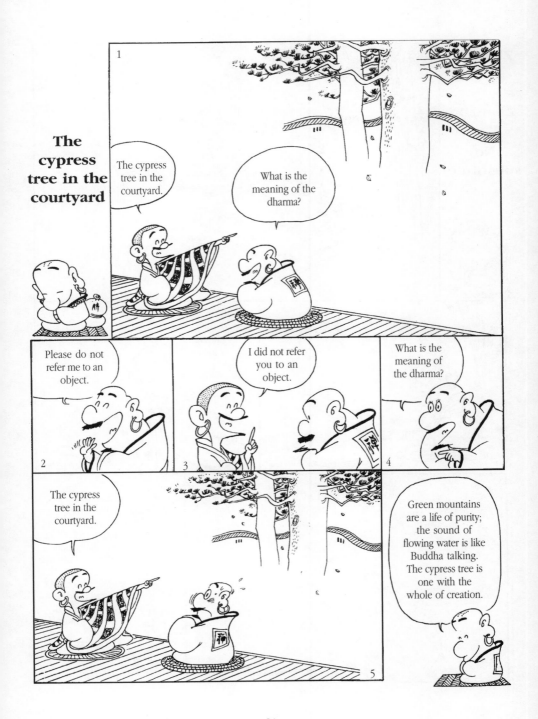

No substitute

82

Deshan Xuanjian (AD 780-865)

A native of Jiannan in Sichuan Province, whose given name was Zhou, he left home early in life.

He was a Buddhist scholar and was especially well-versed in teachings of the Diamond Sutra and had composed a commentary on it. Thus he was also known as Diamond Zhou.

In this sutra, it is said that it requires thousands of world ages of diamond-like concentration and practice for a person to attain buddhahood.

When Deshan heard that the Southern School of Zen held that "mind itself is Buddha," he packed up his commentaries and headed south with the intention – as he thought – of refuting this false teaching.

18

As Deshan received the candle, Longtan blew it out. At that instant, Deshan was enlightened.

19

The following day, Deshan took his Green Dragon commentary to the temple hall and burned it.

Even if we have mastered the profound doctrine, it is only like placing a hair in a vast space. Even if we have exhausted the human knowledge of the world, it is only like letting a drop fall into a great abyss.

20

Once the external light was extinguished, the inner light was able to come into existence. Once dependence on others is gone, then only can one's potential be realized.

Founder of the Linji (Japanese Rinzai) sect
Linji Yixuan (? - AD 867)

Linji was a native of Nanhua in Caozhou district in what is now Shandong Province. His family name was Xing. As a child, he was exceptionally brilliant. He entered a Buddhist monastery as a boy and devoted himself to the study of the Vinaya school and the sutras.

In his early twenties, however, he began to feel an urgent need to grasp the deep meaning of the scriptures through his own experience. He set out on a 2,000-kilometre pilgrimage to seek the instruction of a Southern Zen master. Linji eventually arrived at the monastery of Huangbo Xiyun in Anhui Province.

After his awakening, he travelled and finally settled in the regional capital of Zhengzhou in Henan Province and established the Linji Temple.

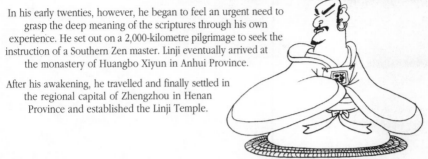

1

Ho!

Strike!

Linji often used a shout ("Ho!") to put a stop to his disciples' dualistic or conceptual thinking. Linji's shout and Deshan's use of the staff were well-known and gave rise to the saying: Linji's shout and Deshan's staff.

As a result, Linji's disciples imitated him and used shouts, although they were ignorant of the purpose.

Ho!

Ho!

2

90

Whiplash

Sometimes a shout is like the precious sword of the Vajraraja (Diamond King); sometimes a shout is like a golden-haired lion that creeps forward in a crouch; sometimes a shout is like a lure stick with a tuft of grass dangling on the end; sometimes a shout is not used as a shout at all.

Linji once told a monk:

1

Do you understand this?

I ...

2

3

Once the distinction between self and others, inside and outside, big and small, good and bad, ignorance and wisdom, life and death, to have and not to have, etc. has been eliminated, then the truth of Zen and insight can be realized. This gives one a new life. To bring this about, one cannot employ thought; one has to use one's own perception.

The monk hesitated and just when he was about to formulate an answer, Linji gave a shout.

Ho!

4

91

Not to be dependent is to be saved

1

One day, Linji went to the pagoda of Bodhidharma (historically the founder of Zen in China).

2

Will you pay your reverence first to Buddha or the Patriarch?

3

Neither to Buddha nor to the Patriarch.

4

What enmity is there between Buddha, Patriarch and you?

5

Linji shook out his long sleeves and left.

Eh?

To seek Buddha's help is to lose Buddha; to seek the Patriarch's help is to lose the Patriarch. The most valuable treasure is with you; it can be found in yourself. Once you seek it outside, you will lose it.

What is living and what is dying?

94

Juzhi's one-finger Zen

Master Juzhi of the Tang Dynasty was from Wuzhou in present-day Zhejiang Province. After he left home to become a monk, he stayed in a hermitage and practised meditation on his own.

1

One day, a nun named Shiji (Reality) came to his hut. Without taking off her rain hat, she walked in a circle three times in front of him.

2

If you can speak, I will take off my rain hat.

3

There must be some Zen revelation in her action, but what exactly is it?

4

Since you cannot give an answer, I will take my leave.

5

What was she trying to convey? What does her rain hat represent?

6

97

Juzhi cuts off disciple's finger

1. This is it.

Juzhi had a servant boy who used to stay at his side and observe him using his one-finger Zen to instruct others ...

2. This is it!

Whenever Juzhi was not around, the servant boy used to answer questions in his place.

3. !

Master, someone came to enquire about the dharma, so I raised my finger to answer on your behalf.

This is like a parrot learning to speak words. What kind of Zen is that?

Arr ...

The poor boy's finger had been cut off!

4.

5.

6. What is the dharma?

7. !

8. The master and the servant boy each raised a finger. The boy saw his shortened finger, and was instantly awakened.

The insight of others is always theirs and can never be made ours unless one can have a perception by oneself.

Xiangyan's man up a tree

1
Xiangyan Zhixian of the Tang Dynasty once said to his disciples: Supposing there is a man who climbed up a tree and held onto a branch with his mouth. Just then somebody comes along and asks him:

2
May I ask what is the supreme meaning of the dharma?

3
If he does not answer, he evades his duty ...

4
If he answers, he will lose his life.

5
Tell me, how is he to resolve such a dilemma?

Ha! Ha! Ha!

6
Let us not ask about the man who is already on the tree. Can you tell me what he was like before he climbed up the tree?

Leading monk Zhao of Hu Tou monastery said:

Regarding the truth that existed before words, one must perceive it with a life that is beyond words.

Same destination, different paths

Too near and cannot see

One day, while Nanquan Puyuan of the Tang Dynasty was cutting grass, a wandering monk asked him for directions:

May I ask how to get to the famous temple of Nanquan?

I spent thirty coins to buy this sickle.

I am not asking you about the sickle, but how to go to Nanquan's temple.

This sickle proves to be very sharp when used.

One who is caught in thought loses one's original nature. All he knows are words and descriptions; when he sees the actual thing he fails to perceive it.

The universe in a mustard seed

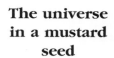

1 During the Tang Dynasty, there was a person named Li Bo who was very fond of reading books. Because he read extensively, he was nicknamed "Ten-thousand-volume Li." Once, he asked the monk Guizong Zhichang:

2 The Vimalakirti-nirdea Sutra says: "Mount Sumeru (the phenomenal world) contains in it a mustard seed and a mustard seed contains in it Mount Sumeru." The first statement I can readily believe but as to the second, can it be more than a senseless tale?

3 Er ...

Everybody calls you "Ten-thousand-volume Li." May I ask how those ten thousand volumes of books can be contained in your little skull?

Many worldly intellectuals just study Zen for something to talk about, something that will enhance their reputation. They consider this a lofty interest, and try to use it to assert their superiority over others. This only increases their egotism.

The monk who lacks compassion

1 There was an old woman who supported a monk for twenty years. She had built a little hut for him and fed him while he was practising meditation.

Amitabha Buddha.

2 A pretty lass used to bring food to the monk and attended to him while he meditated.

3 Afterwards, when you send food to him, embrace him to test the outcome of his meditation.

Alright.

How do you feel?

It is like an old tree that grows on a cold rock in winter; like the absence of a feeling of warmth in the depth of winter.

4

5

6 All I have supported for twenty years is but an unremarkable fellow!

When the old woman heard this, she drove the monk out of the hut and burned it down.

Of course, monks are not supposed to lust after women, but after practising meditation for twenty years the monk did not have a compassionate heart. Truly an unremarkable bum!

True self, awake!

1
The Zen master Ruiyan Shiyan of the Tang Dynasty was given to talking to himself every now and then.

2
True self!

3
Yes!

4
Awaken yourself!

5
Yes! Yes!

6
Do not be deceived by others!

7
Yes! Yes!

Man is often at the mercy of circumstances and is confused and agitated because of the lack of inner clarity and the scars left by past experiences. Everyone has to be deeply aware of oneself and thus be master of oneself.

Simple truth but difficult to follow

Ordinary-mindedness is the way

No me, no other

1 Yunyan Tansheng went to visit Tang Dynasty Zen Master Baizhang Huaihai, who was the monastery's abbot. Baizhang is famous for the saying: "A day without work, a day without food."

You work so hard every day, and for whose sake?

There is someone who requires it.

2

Why not have him do it himself?

3

He does not have the wherewithal to do it.

4

Self and other - this form of dualistic thinking is the source of sorrow. One has to have a compassionate heart that does not discriminate between self and other, and help the one who needs help most.

113

Not seeing the truth

An official named Wei asked Zen master Xuansha Shibei of the Tang Dynasty:

Somebody said we use "it" all the time, but do not know what "it" is. What thing is this?

1

Have some fruit.

Thank you.

Yummy!

Master, you have not answered me. What thing is this?

2

3

4

It is this. You use it every day but do not know what it is.

"It is not difficult to understand the Tao, only do not discriminate and choose." If you ask where is the path to understanding, you are making a great mistake. This is because there is no path – we are living in the midst of Tao.

5

115

To lack nothing

Shitou Xiqian of the Tang Dynasty was a disciple of the Sixth Patriarch Huineng, who taught at Caoxi.

From Caoxi, where Huineng taught.

Where do you come from?

What did you learnt at Caoxi?

That I lacked nothing before I went to Caoxi.

If I did not go to Caoxi, then how would I know that I lack nothing?

No teacher can confer insight on a disciple, but he can help a disciple to understand all at once and have insight by himself.

Then why did you go to Caoxi?

* Together with Mazu Daoyi, Shitou was a great teacher of over 160 enlightened disciples. In his boyhood, Shitou showed unusual character, once destroying a sacrificial altar in a Liao aboriginal village and leading away an ox that was to be killed.

Beyond words

There is and there is not

1

Is there paradise and hell?

Yes.

Scholar Zhangzhou asked Zen master Xitang Chizang of the Tang Dynasty:

2

That is not correct. I once asked Master Qinshan Wensui about Zen, and all he said was "nothing."

3

Mister, how many family relations do you have?

A wife and two children.

4

5

And how many family relations does Qinshan have?

Mister, you speak from the standpoint of being a family man. You must be like Qinshan before you can say all is "nothing."

There is variation in everything. Therefore there is no "fixed standard" in the world; it varies with a person's circumstances.

6

Qinshan is a monk who has left home, how could he have family relations?

7

Follow the flow

1 After Tang Dynasty Zen master Damei Fachang's enlightenment, he secluded himself in a mountaintop hermitage for thirty years before accepting disciples.

2 One day, a novice monk who had lost his way came upon Damei.

3 I only see the surrounding mountains changing from green to yellow with the seasons.

How long have you been living here?

4 Which path can I take to get out of this mountain?

5 Follow the flow.

Action is actually very easy. But it is often circumscribed by self-imposed restrictions, making even the slightest movement of freedom difficult.

119

Monk without a sense of humour

Baiyun Shouduan of the Song Dynasty was very diligent, but he lacked a sense of humour.

Which teacher did you previously study under?

Once, his master Yangqi Fanghui asked him:

Master Yue of Chaling.

I heard that while crossing a bridge, he fell into the water and was enlightened. He wrote a gatha about it.

I still remember the contents of the gatha.

I have one jewel shining bright.

Long buried it was underneath worldly worries.
This morning the dusty veil is off and restored is its lustre.

Illuming rivers and mountains and ten thousand things.

Ha!
Ha!
Ha!

1
2
3
4
5
6
7

Panel 8: Ha! Ha!

Panel 9: Shouduan could not understand why his teacher burst into laughter and did not sleep the whole night.

Panel 10: The next morning.... Master, why did you laugh after hearing Master Yue's gatha?

Panel 11: Yes, I did. Did you see the exorcists in the street yesterday? Master, what are you referring to? In what way are you no better than the exorcists?

Panel 13: When Shouduan heard this, he was enlightened. The exorcists want people to laugh, but you are afraid of people laughing.

Zen is beyond the state of logic. Its practice is to examine thoroughly the life of a common person, and to steer clear of stifling rigidity and abstraction.

Danxia burning a Buddha statue

Zen master Danxia Tianran of the Tang Dynasty was once at Huiling Temple and because it was extremely cold that day, he burnt a statue of Buddha to keep warm ...

1

How dare you burn a statue of Buddha?

2

3

I am trying to see if I can find any sharira* by burning a statue of Buddha.

4

Er ...

How can you expect to find sharira in a wooden statue?

If there are no sharira to be found in it, then let me have the remaining two Buddha statues for my fire.

A man of Tao has no self, so how can he be guilty of wrongdoing? To act without any sense of self is to be free of wrongdoing.

5

* sharira: some indestructible substance, generally in pebble form, said to be found in the body of a holy man when it is cremated.

123

Oneness with the universe

Change is the eternal truth

1 Master, the physical body rots away; is there a truth that never changes and is eternal?

Yes, there is.

2 It is like the beautiful flowers on the mountain, as lovely as brocade ...

It is like the calm water in the stream; actually it is flowing.

Flowers wither easily, yet they never cease to bloom; the water in the gully is constantly flowing, yet the stream seems unchanging. The meaning of life can be realized in the process of living. Change is the eternal truth.

3

127

The way to truth is right before you

A Zen pupil asked Master Yuezhou Qianfeng of the Tang Dynasty:

All buddhas of the ten parts of the universe enter the one road of nirvana. Where does that road begin?

Right here.

The meaning of life is not to be found in a distant world of abstraction, but in paying attention to everyday happenings and details of one's life. One's perception has to be in the field of living. In contemplating where the truth may be found, it just might be right before you.

The nun becomes a monk

* There is a traditional belief that enlightenment is only for men.

Three pounds of hemp

Bamboo of the South, wood of the North.

The more I hear, the more I do not understand.

6

Thus the monk went back to Dongshan to find out from him.

7

Words do not express facts, speech does not accord with the situation. Those who accept words are lost, and those who linger over phrases are deluded.

8

It can be likened to the situation where a stone strikes a dog. The dog then turns to look at the stone that struck its body. But if a stone strikes a lion, the lion disregards the stone and charges at the person who threw it. One must not be like the dog but be like the lion in Zen practice.

9

The Zen practitioner's utterances are but words suited for the occasion, a kind of "word head" (leading phrase) that draws one into a deeper realm. One must not think that the literal meaning is what Zen is all about.

135

Buffalo passing through a window

Zen master Wuzu Fayan of the Song Dynasty described this situation: A buffalo passes through a window.

The horns and the four legs go past.

Only the tail does not pass through.

A person may resolve to give up worldly things and undergo hardship to practise Zen, but the desire for fame is still there. Such a person still has traces of weakness, like a buffalo which passes through the window but whose tail fails to get through. Having such blind spots, one cannot be considered perceptive.

To be
master
of
oneself

1

Nature begets all things,

2

The formless is by nature alone yet complete and silent,

3

To be like a master to all things,

4

And to go beyond time.

Humans are in essence one with the whole. A person who sees that one is not separated from the whole is the Tao, Buddha, and the spirit of Zen. To be master of oneself, one must not regard environment and circumstances as obstacles, but change oneself.

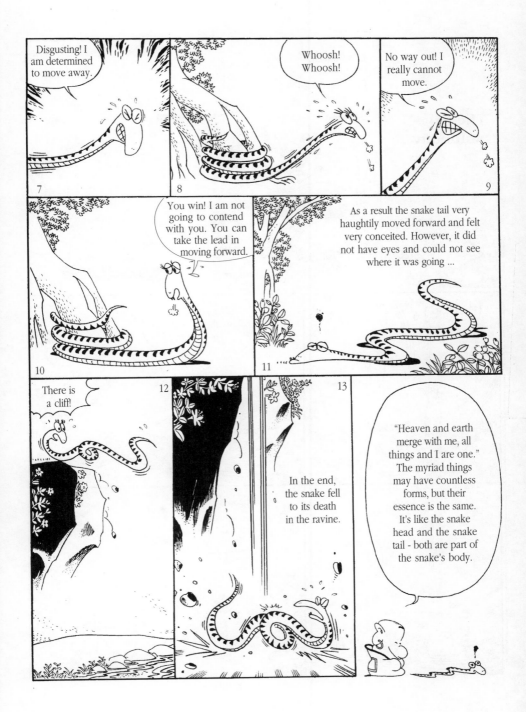

The frogs' soliloquy

143

The spider's lifeline

This is a parable. Shakyamuni Buddha was once sitting by a well in a garden when he gazed into the well.

1

Wah! Wah!

2

Save me! I am suffering greatly. Save me!

3

When this man was living, he committed many atrocities, so he went into hell after death.

4

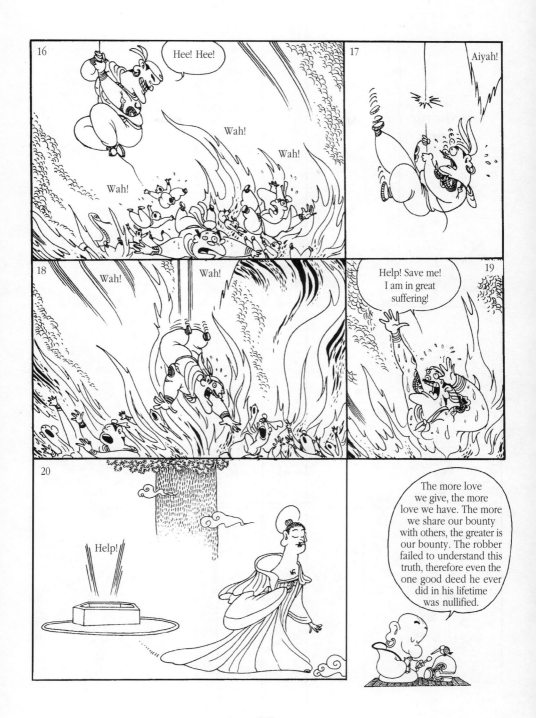

16
Hee! Hee!
Wah!
Wah!
Wah!
17
Aiyah!
18
Wah!
Wah!
19
Help! Save me! I am in great suffering!
20
Help!
The more love we give, the more love we have. The more we share our bounty with others, the greater is our bounty. The robber failed to understand this truth, therefore even the one good deed he ever did in his lifetime was nullified.

150

Chinese Philosophy in Comics
by Tsai Chih Chung

Art of War

Art of War provides a compact set of principles essential for victory in battles; applicable to military strategising, in business and human relationships.

Book of Zen

Zen makes the art of spontaneous living the prime concern of the human being. Tsai Chih Chung depicts Zen with unfettered versatility; his illustrations span a period of more than 2,000 years.

Origins of Zen

In this book, Tsai Chih Chung traces the origins and development of Zen in China with a light-hearted touch which is very much in keeping with the Zen spirit of absolute freedom and unbounded creativity.

Roots of Wisdom

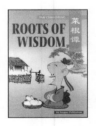

One of the gems of Chinese literature, whose advocacy of a steadfast nature and a life of simplicity, goodness, quiet joy and harmony with one's fellow beings and the world at large has great relevance in an age of rapid changes.

Sayings of Confucius

This book features the life of Confucius, selected sayings from *The Analects* and some of his more prominent pupils. It captures the warm relationship between the sage and his disciples, and offers food for thought to the modern readers.

Sayings of Han Fei Zi

Tsai Chih Chung retells and interprets the basic ideas of legalism, a classical political philosophy that advocates a draconian legal code, embodying a system of liberal reward and heavy penalty as the basis of government, in his unique style.

Sayings of Lao Zi

Tsai Chih Chung has presented the thoughts of Lao Zi in a light-hearted and entertaining manner. He has provided readers with a fast and easy way to understanding the Taoist classic *Dao De Jing*, and has given this renowned literature a fresh appeal.

Sayings of Lie Zi

A famous Taoist sage whose sayings deal with universal themes such as the joy of living, reconciliation with death, the limitations of human knowledge as well as the role of chance events.

Sayings of Mencius

This book contains stories about the life of Mencius and various excerpts from *Mencius*, one of the *Four Books of the Confucian Classics*, which contains the philosophy of Mencius.

Sayings of Zhuang Zi

This comic on Taoism is no longer seen as an escapist philosophy of those who keep away from the hustle and bustle of society, but as a most natural foundation for a life of calm and quiet strength in an ever-changing world.

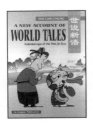

New Account of World Tales

120 selected anecdotes in this book tell the stories of emperors, princes, high officials, generals, courtiers, urbane monks, and the lettered gentry of a turbulent time. They afford a stark and amoral insight into human behaviour in its full spectrum of virtues and frailties.

Records of the Historian

Records of the Historian, written by Sima Qian of the Han Dynasty, provides a realistic picture of many different historical figures and aspects of Han society. In this book, Tsai has illustrated the life and characteristics of the Four Lords of the Warring States.

The Illustrated Heart Sutra

Written in only 260 Chinese characters, the *Heart Sutra* contains the most profound wisdom in Buddhism. Here, Buddhism is presented not as a religion but as the accumulated wisdom of "enlightened ones" who contemplated the trials and mysteries of life.

Sayings of Buddha

This conpendium of Buddha's lessons — dynamically illuminated by Tsai Chih Chung — provides practical guidelines for disciplining the mind and behaviour.

The Illustrated Dharma Sutra

The Dharma, or the Law, is the body of essential truths of the universe and human life. The Buddha describes the path to spiritual cultivation in a simple yet captivating way. Tsai Chih Chung's illumination of the *Dhammapada* communicates to each of us these truths and shows us how to practise them.

Hilarious Chinese Classics
by Tsai Chih Chung

Romance of the Three Kingdoms

Set in the turbulent Three Kingdoms Period, *Romance of the Three Kingdoms* relates the clever political manoeuvres and brilliant battle strategies used by the ambitious rulers as they fought one another for supremacy. The events of the story provide lessons in warfare, politics and human psychology.

Outlaws of the Marsh

The seven outlaws featured in this comic edition were fugitives in the eyes of the law, but heroes in their own right. For instance, Tiger Slayer Wu Song killed his adulterous sister-in-law because she had poisoned his brother.

Madam White Snake

Most of you may be familiar with the story of Madam White Snake. But do you know that Xiaoqing, Madam White Snake's faithful maid, was actually a carp? Or that the self-righteous monk Fa Hai was actually a toad? Tsai Chih Chung injects much wit and humour into this modern interpretation of an age-old tale.

The Drunken Fox

These three humorous stories promise to leave you in stitches!
THE DRUNKEN FOX tells the story of how a fox spirit turns the world topsy-turvy with his madcap antics.
THE CROW BROTHERS chronicles the struggles of a dumb-man-and-bright-bird duo as they tumble from one adventure to the next.
THE DRAGON KING'S DAUGHTER recounts the tale of how a scholar rescues the Dragon Princess from a life of drudgery.

Three Incarnations

The feud between two people escalate and stretch over these incarnations — an official and a commoner; a cat and a dog; and a father-in-law and his son-in-law! This work, Tsai-styled, will amuse you with its witty fantasies.

Journey to the West: The Magnificent Monkey King
Journey to the West: The Incredible Journey

These books offer more than the all-too-familiar escapades of Tang Sanzang and his animal disciples. Under the creative pen of Tsai Chih Chung, *Journey to the West* still stays its course but takes a new path. En route from ancient China to India to acquire Buddhist scriptures, the Monk and his disciples veer off course frequently to dart into modern times for fleeting exchanges with characters ranging from Ronald Reagan to Bunny Girls of the Playboy Club.

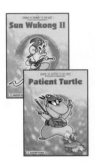

Sequel to Journey to the West: Sun Wukong II
(Previously known as Sequel to Journey to the West Bk 1)
Sequel to Journey to the West: Going West
(Previously known as Sequel to Journey to the West Bk 2)
Sequel to Journey to the West: Demons Yin & Yang
(Previously known as Sequel to Journey to the West Bk 3)
Sequel to Journey to the West: Patient Turtle
(Previously known as Sequel to Journey to the West Bk 4)

Tsai's cartoon series combines the original pilgrimage story with its creative satire based on current events. His exceptional sense of wit and humour makes the stories wacky enough to have you tickled pink.

Shaolin Temple

Set against the respectable Shaolin Temple, readers are treated to endless humour that threatens to have them collapsing on the floor in stitches. Cheer the participants on as they do their utmost in a martial arts tournament. Study the many imaginatively-named martial skills on display. Check out the eye-popping weapons used. It will be the best match you have ever attended!

Creation of the Gods: *Ne Zha Wreaks Havoc & Jiang Ziya Displays His Prowess*

Another Chinese classic gem cut into hilarious perfection by Tsai! Watch Ne Zha, Jiang Taigong, the debauched King Zhou of Shang, his evil concubine Daji, King Wen of Zhou, Huang Feihu and other unforgettable characters make cameo appearances on Earth and take on modern issues with new comic twists and turns.

All-round Series

Books dedicated to contemporary lifestyle,
guiding us in adapting to the modern world

Other books in the series...

PROSPECT: Mapping Out Your Future
This book is about facing your future, planning your destiny and working towards your personal goals. Besides exploring the meaning of life and the future of individuals, it also looks at the future of enterprises and their employees.

SUCCESS WITH WEALTH AND JOY
Success is a concept; wealth, a duty; happiness, a right. The author challenges the conventional notion of success, discusses how to strike a balance between self-affirmation and the realities of life, and examines how to deal with wealth (or the lack of it).

BE A CAT: Declaration of the New Millennium
The 21st century belongs to the cat — the truly independent and individualistic creature. Author Tsai Chih Chung argues for a change in our mindset and shares his vision for success in the new era.

BE A WINNER: Get Going and Enjoy Life's Victories
This book will show you the secrets to becoming a winner. At the same time, it conveys an important message: Success is *not* about wealth accumulation and power acquisition. No one, except yourself, can define what success means to you.

LEADERSHIP: A Dose of Sun Zi
What are the signal leadership qualities in a general who can lead his men wholeheartedly to battle and even death? Besides answering this question, the author also applies the wisdom of a 2,000-year-old Chinese military classic to modern management leadership.

FUTURE OF THE MEDIA
A technopreneur, the author cuts through the fog of highbrow tech-speak and shares in layman terms all you need to know about media and technology — that's what the future is all about! Seize control of the media today!

FUTURE OF EDUCATION
The author shows how computer technology can be harnessed to make quality changes and rectify present drawbacks as well as open up exciting new opportunities in the development of human potential. Recommended for teachers, parents and educationists.

FUTURE OF THE ENTERPRISE

Sayling Wen expounds on the "wings of competitiveness" — the 8 Cs — the first three being core competence, end customer and continuous creation. He argues that in this wired generation, *SPEED* is crucial — how fast a business delivers its core competence to its end customer, and how well it innovates to ensure a continuous stream of profit.

FUTURE OF E-COMMERCE

The advent of the network age has resulted in a whole new wired economy. The author illustrates how building e-commerce activities on top of traditional commerce will make the products / services more efficient and visible and at the same time, provide the convenience of product testing on the Internet.

Be Happy Today! Asiapac's All-round books can make it happen.

Order Form			
Title	Qty	*Price S$	Total
Prospect: Mapping Out Your Future		$ 8.60	
Success with Wealth and Joy		$ 8.60	
Be A Cat: Declaration of the New Millennium		$ 8.60	
Be A Winner: Get Going and Enjoy Life's Victories		$ 8.60	
Leadership: A Dose of Sun Zi		$ 8.60	
Future of the Media		$ 8.60	
Future of Education		$ 8.60	
Future of Enterprise		$ 8.60	
Future of E-commerce		$ 8.60	

Nett prices indicated after discount (GST incl.). Free postage for Singapore only.
Note: For overseas orders, please include postage fees:
Surface mail: S$5.00 for every book. Air mail: S$8.00 for every book.
I wish to purchase the above-mentioned titles at the nett price of S$ _____

Enclosed is my postal order/money order/cheque for S$ _____ (No.: _____)
Name (Mr/Mrs/Ms) _____ Tel _____
Address _____
_____ Fax _____
Please charge the amount of S$ _____ to my VISA/MASTER CARD account
(only Visa/Master Card accepted)
Card No. _____ Card Expiry Date _____

Card Holder's Name _____ Signature _____

Send to: **ASIAPAC BOOKS PTE LTD**
            996 Bendemeer Road #06-08/09 Singapore 339944 Tel: 6392 8455 Fax: 6392 6455
Note: Prices quoted valid for purchase by mail order only. Prices subject to change without prior notice.

禅说

编著 ：蔡志忠
翻译 ：许国强

亚太图书有限公司出版